Dedication

To my friends and family who continue to support and encourage me in my efforts.

To Sheryll Murray who drew the front cover for the book.

To Stuart Diamond who continues to be my technical and computer advisor.

Without these people this book would never have been possible.

THE BRIDE WORE RED

By Louella Murphy

CHAPTER 1   The Bride Wore Red

My hand shook a little with excitement as I carefully went over the eight in 1928 on my hospital birth certificate to change it into a six. Applying gentle pressure, I used an eraser on the tiny space of the first number until it disappeared, changing my age from fourteen to sixteen. Relaxing now I sat back and took a deep breath. The first step was successfully completed. I had proof that I was of age to get married without parental consent in Idaho.

A noise from downstairs caused me to push the newly altered document under the school homework I was supposedly working on, and call out "Mommy, you're home early. I'll be right down."

Mommy turned from spooning coffee grounds into the pot on the stove as I entered and said, "Sadie had her car so I didn't have to wait for the bus. It was pretty quiet tonight so we got out quickly. I'll put my feet up and read for a while. You going out?"

"Not tonight. We're going swimming in Hot Springs tomorrow night after work. Chuck can pick me up at the drive-in with Bobby and Jocelyn so I'll pack my suit and towel tonight and take it with me tomorrow."

I got a glass of milk from the icebox and returned to my room as I mentally ran through the list of things to be remembered. The birth certificate went on the bottom of the bag I usually used for swimming dates. The ID to prove my increased age was covered by my favorite blue, two-piece swimsuit, our best towel, and a comb, brush and lipstick. Ready.

The red suit that Chuck had bought for me last week, black dressy shoes, two changes of traveling clothes and underwear, with bobby pins, hair curlers and a bar of soap were already in a small suitcase in the trunk of Bobby's car. Our best friends were the only ones in on our plans.

We often went to Hot Springs where an indoor – outdoor pool and adjoining restaurant allowed us to swim in the warm mineral waters and get a snack or meal after. It was a favorite dating place for young and old, but usually not crowded on weeknights.

The next day went as planned through school, four hours work at the Snack Shack, and Chuck's arrival in his father's car. Chuck said he told his father Bobby was having car trouble so he could get the car. It was no problem since their family had two, both Buicks, and Chuck was allowed the use of one when he was home from school during the summer. We changed and entered the pool quickly after we arrived, racing around the inside area and out into the chill air of the outside pool. The moon was full and our mood was pure joy.

"How did you guys get here so soon?" came from Jocelyn as our friends joined us. "You must have driven really fast."

"Practicing for the drive to Boise." Chuck grinned as he splashed water toward her.

The next hour was spent playing in the water and reveling in the excitement of impending adventure. We all knew our lives would be changed forever by this elopement, and we had talked about possible consequences. Our decision had been made and we never thought of looking back. Chuck and Bobby had received their draft notices and would be leaving in two weeks. I was afraid of losing him, and desperately wanted to get away from my home and my father. Of course, I loved Chuck with all the intensity of first love and fourteen years.

Time to leave and we prepared by transferring our clothes from Bobby's trunk to Chuck's. Our wet suits and towels went into Bobby's trunk. My biggest regret for many years was I never got back my favorite swimsuit. It got forgotten and stayed in that trunk until someone cleaned the car and threw everything out.

"Goodbye. We'll be back in two days. Remember to call Dad early tomorrow so they won't worry. Tell him I'll take good care of the car." Chuck turned from Bobby and opened the car door.

"Josie, tell Mommy I'm sorry but I'll be back, and I couldn't let Chuck leave without showing how much I love him. She'll have to tell Daddy. Try to be out of the house before in case he gets real mad. You know if he's drunk you never can tell" We had no phone in our house so my friend would have to go there before school in the morning. Quick hugs all around and I got into the car.

We pulled out onto the highway and turned north toward Idaho. I sat back and looked over at the eighteen year old man I was choosing to spend the rest of my life with. Next stop Boise.

CHAPTER 2   Boise

I leaned back against the seat cushions and looked sideways at Chuck driving the car. His hands were steady and sure on the wheel and he focused on the road ahead as the miles passed behind us. He gave me a quick glance and said, "I love you so much."

I reached out and touched his arm quickly and said, "Me too."

This was really happening! We were on our way to get married. I looked at his profile as he returned his full concentration again to his driving. He was handsome with a smooth, clean look to his features, and a muscular six foot frame. His hair was a medium brown, and his skin pale and unblemished. I felt a thrill buzz through me at the wonderful luck that I was going to be married to this very special man. How had this happened?

Chuck said, "Sit back and rest. It's a long drive. Sleep if you can. I'll wake you if I begin to get sleepy and you can keep me awake."

I snuggled down in the seat as I smiled at him and started reflecting on the past four years which had led to this elopement. My parents, with my little sister Lonnie and me, had traveled from Joplin Missouri to Ogden, Utah by hitchhiking. When money and necessary supplies ran short, they would find some kind of work and shelter until they could save enough to once again resume our travel west. There was some vague idea of eventually getting to California where the sun always shone and there was always work to be found.

The trip started when I was seven, and when we made it to Ogden, I had just become ten years old. I learned many things along the way about living and about people and values. Reading was always my entertainment and escape, and I liked learning from the different cultures and environments we encountered along the way. I was skipped forward in school as we went from state to state and wound up being grouped with kids older than myself.

In Utah we found work and friendship and put down roots which became permanent. I indulged in the process of becoming a teenager, and at fourteen was a junior in high school and physically grown. I grew from football and other group games to parties playing post office, to dating, mostly in groups. We rented horses and rode through the woods and hills above town with picnic lunches. We drove to Hot Springs and swam and played in the warm mineral pools all year round. We hiked in the mountains and canyons starting just east of town. In winter we donned ice skates and skated on the ponds and streams flowing from those mountains. Some of us got jobs after school which enabled us to have spending money and to buy our own clothes and school supplies. My father signed a certificate saying I was two years older than my actual age and half my wages went to him.

Chuck was my first real love, joining our group when he came home for the summer from his school in Minnesota. His family lived on the Bench, which was the wealthy area east of town, and as the only boy in his family he was sent away to attend the all boy's high school his father and other male members of his extended family had gone. Graduating this year, he had returned to take his place in his father's business.

Then he met me. And now I would be a part of that family, with his four sisters, his mother and father. I would learn to live with and have things I had only dreamed of. Most important I would have this wonderful man to spend my life with. I drifted off to sleep treasuring that thought.

"Wake up honey. We're almost there." Chuck was gently shaking my shoulder as I sat up and looked out the window.

We were in a residential area on the outskirts of a town, so I sat up and brushed back my hair, blinking my eyes to drive away the sleep. Chuck still seemed awake and alert though dawn was breaking and he had driven through the night. In a few minutes we pulled up to a hotel and took our bags out of the trunk. He had pre-registered so they were expecting us.

I looked up the block to the sign 'Town Hall' where we would go after some sleep and cleaning up and changing clothes. Then I giggled with joy, hugged him, and we walked into the lobby of the Boise Hotel.

CHAPTER 3   Married

We entered the lobby of the Boise Hotel and stopped a minute to look around. It was empty at three o'clock in the morning, and the bellman was lounging on a bench to the left of the door, while we could see the clerk behind his desk focused on a magazine. There were couches, and a few chairs around the walls, and stairs at the back of the room leading to the second floor. A hallway to the right of them led to the rooms on the main floor.

I had never been in a hotel before, and the place seemed luxurious to me. I followed Chuck across the room to where the clerk looked up our reservations and was paid in advance for two nights. He summoned the bellman who advanced and took our bags saying, "Good morning, please follow me."

We went down the hallway, he deposited our bags on the floor inside the room and told us "The café next door opens at six for breakfast and stays open till mid-night. If you want anything just come to the desk and they'll help you." Chuck gave him some coins and he left.

We stood back and looked at each other, happy but suddenly a little shy. We hugged, then Chuck said, "We should get some sleep, it was a long drive and we don't have to get up early." He lifted the bags up on the bed and opened them. We took our clothes out and hung them, then I went into the washroom and put on the pretty new nightgown I had bought the week before for this occasion. I climbed into bed and snuggled under the comforter while Chuck changed into pajamas.

We both fell asleep quickly, and slept until almost noon, then proceeded to dress carefully for the event of the day. The new red suit Chuck had bought me was softly tailored and fit perfectly. I had invested in black heeled pumps and a purse, with white earrings and necklace. I looked older than the sixteen I was supposed to be. Chuck wore a grey suit with a red tie and carried his handsome six-foot person with a mature self-assurance.

"I'm too excited to eat anything. Let's come back for breakfast after," I said.

"Good idea," Chuck smiled at me. "I couldn't eat either."

We didn't take the car out but walked down the block to the town hall, where we were directed to the office for wedding licenses by a pleasant older lady. The clerk asked to see our identification and I presented the carefully altered birth certificate. "Oh, 16, all right." She said as she smiled and handed me the form to fill out. The process was repeated with Chuck after he showed her his Draft notice, and we filled out names, addresses and ages. Then she took us to the Justice of the Peace office and introduced him to us.

He asked her to stay, and called another clerk to be witness, then showed us where to stand in front of his desk. "We are gathered here to witness the joining of this man and this woman in matrimony, which is a holy estate ....".

My head was spinning and I felt weak. Everyone was smiling - I saw tears in the eyes of the older clerk; this wonderful man was holding my hand tight. My throat was so tight I could barely manage to whisper the "I do" when the time came. This was not a dream. It was really happening!!!

Then the ladies were hugging us, and the Justice was shaking our hands. Congratulations and best wishes were coming from everywhere. We walked out of the town hall into crisp November sunlight and headed back to the café for our wedding breakfast.

Mr. and Mrs. Ellis. I was now legally a grown up married woman with a new life ahead.

CHAPTER 4   A New Life

We awoke in the morning to a fresh snowfall and the promise of a bright day to begin our married life. After a quick breakfast next door to the hotel we set out to explore the downtown area of Boise consisting of three saloons, a large hardware/feed and grain store, the hotel, courthouse, two eateries, a Newbury "five and dime" and the newest structure, a J. C. Penny department store. We chose that store to visit for spending our meager funds on trinkets to bring home to our families.

"Oh look, a little doll dressed in overalls, Erica would love it." Chuck agreed and $.50 cents went. Next came ornamental hair clips for Maxine, who had waist length hair she liked to braid and fasten up. "Let's get books for Sharon and Donna. They have picture books, story books, and they both like to read."

This was a special treat for me because I knew his family had stock in the company, and because I had never been in a position to shop in a "department store" before. It was fascinating to wander around the displays from clothing to kitchen pots and pans to shoes, outdoor tools etc, all under one roof. We spent a long time making choices for his four sisters and my sister and for our mothers. My sister Lonnie got a pretty comb and brush set, then we agonized over our mothers before choosing warm scarves for both of them. Our fathers were an easy decision since we knew both of them enjoyed wine, so we chose brands they may not have tasted before.

Returning to the hotel we rested a while, then dressed for our first dinner as married people. Chuck said "Let's not go to the hotel restaurant. We can try someplace else." We walked a couple of blocks to the largest saloon which boasted a dance hall and restaurant. He ordered from the menu while I marveled over the many choices. "Dance, Mrs. Ellis." And we dance to the piano music until the waiter told us our food was ready.

I had my first taste of fresh oysters and found them not as good as the canned ones my mother sometimes got. The steak surrounded by fluffy mashed potatoes was a treat. It was my first experience of food prepared for looks as well as taste, and the dessert presentation with choices of cake, pie, cookies, puddings made for a lifelong impression of fine dining.

Upon our return to the hotel, Chuck prepared to settled with the hotel, since we intended to leave well before daylight in the morning. On discovering we had spent more than planned, he went down to send a telegram to his parents, "Please send some money. We're married but we don't have enough money to get home" We packed while we waited for an answer and took suitcases to the car which we had earlier filled with gas. After an anxious two hours a money order arrived, enough to settle the hotel charges and for gas. Then we settled in early for a good sleep in preparation for the long drive home to face our consequences.

Charles had called and talked with his Mother early in the morning so we knew my family had been told. Chuck told me " She said our fathers were ready to come after us in anger, but after some drinking together discovered they liked each other and wound up celebrating instead." His family was ready to welcome us and I would live with them in Chucks room, even after he left for the service. His sisters were thrilled, our mothers, not so much. But they were accepting of the inevitable and hoping for the best.

We had an uneventful drive home talking about our plans after the war ended and he was safely back from his travels. I ignored the sick scared hole in my stomach about facing my Mother, but knowing I was now safe from my Father's punishment. No more whippings! The man by my side was my love, my savior, my protector for life. I was truly grown up and married!

CHAPTER 5 New York Trip

"It won't be that long. I'll get leave before I'm shipped out and it depends where I'm sent whether you can come and stay there with me" Chuck said.

I choked back the tears as I hugged him again and answered, "Hope you go to California. Warm all the time, I would like. "

He gave me another kiss before turning to board the train with other young men heading for New York to be assigned to the positions their evaluations qualified them for. The Merchant Marine was a major factor in the war, transporting goods and sometimes troops to destinations very near the combat zones. They were unarmed targets for enemy ships and planes, and usually escorted by armed Navy ships.

The crowd of relatives stood and waved the train out of sight, then Chuck's oldest sister Tara put her arm around me and we returned to the car and home. The rest of the family had said their good-byes at home before we left for the early morning departure and were waiting breakfast until we returned. We sat and ate. There was no conversation.

The business of eating finished, I started clearing the dishes into the sink while Chuck's father left for his office and his four sisters got ready and left for school. His mother started her cleaning while I finished cleaning the kitchen. Then she called, "Come sit down. We need to talk."

My stomach dropped and I trembled a little as I crossed to the living room and dropped into the chair across from her. She smiled at me as she asked "What are we going to do now? Are you planning to go back to school, or get a job?"

I relaxed a little as I realized she was not going to yell at me and began to decide what my immediate future should be. "Chuck and I talked about that before he left. Going back to school is not possible. They might not allow it since I'm married now. Anyhow it would be too awkward. I thought I'd apply at Hill Field Air Force Base. The factory out there is always looking for more workers and I took typing last year."

Two weeks later I was getting up at five to have breakfast, get dressed and walk a block to the corner. There I got picked up by a neighbor who drove three other girls to the factory each morning. We were all drop-outs for varying reasons and I learned a lot on the rides to and from work. They came from different social and cultural backgrounds and shared living situations I had never encountered or considered before. I didn't talk much about myself, only that I was just married and my new husband had left for the service, as most young men were doing. I certainly wasn't revealing that I was only fourteen and working under an altered birth certificate.

Letters from Chuck were cheerful and positive. He had been selected to be trained as a pharmacist's mate and would be in Brooklyn Navy Yard Maritime school for six months after he completed basic boot camp. He liked the barracks and the men he had met and was kept too busy to get homesick. Though he missed me, he was proud to be doing his part for the war effort. He wouldn't get leave to go off the base until completion of basics but was looking forward to exploring New York City and wished I could be there to share that.

My life settled into a routine of work, occasional movies with Chuck's sisters, and visits with my family. Mommy and Chuck's mother became friends and shared challenges of daily living from their very different lifestyles. Mommy worked at the hospital, which was near Chuck's house, so she sometimes stopped in on her way home for a short visit. On my day off I would walk the two miles to our house to have Sunday dinner with Mommy and my little sister. Daddy, when he was there, said very little to me.

Two months passed and I realized I was pregnant. When I wrote to Chuck I was scared. This had not figured into our vague plans for "after the war'" and we had little idea about the whole process. He would live on base until schooling was done then would ship out for duty, transporting freight and/or troops to action locations. The pay he received was enough to cover personal items and needs but definitely no way to support a family. I had been saving every penny I made for our nest-egg when he came home. I felt desperate and alone.

We made the decision that I should come to New York and get an apartment, and we would be able to spend each week-end pass together. Some of his shipmates had this arrangement already and were comfortable with it. I had plenty of money for bus fare and to support myself until I could get a job, I thought. The announcement to the families met with some concern, but both families believed you sleep in the bed you make, so they wished us good luck and helped me pack one large suitcase and a small bag with what I would need for a four day ride. Within a week I was on a Greyhound Bus heading across the country to New York City.

CHAPTER 6   New Life Begins

It was ten at night when the bus pulled into its parking space in Grand Central Station. The last two hours seemed an almost unbroken series of lights from stores, increasingly larger buildings and occasional scarce residential areas as we drew deeper into the heart of New York City. After days spent riding across the country, looking out on fields of farmland, rock cliffs, mountain peaks and the small cities and settlements of rest stops across two thousand miles of our country, we had arrived!

I was filled with the heart squeezing excitement of walking out into an unknowable environment as I waited at the side of the bus for my big suitcase. I said good-bye to the last of the four drivers who had brought us safely through the last leg of the journey and listened carefully as he directed me to the Travelers Aid kiosk located inside the huge main waiting room. My smaller bag and purse were crossed over my chest with shoulder straps and secured by my belt on the outside of the straps as I had been instructed by my own and by Chuck's mother. I dragged the large, heavy suitcase toward the kiosk.

The woman sitting in the chair looked up with a smile, "Can I help you?"

"I was told to come to you for a place to stay. I just came off the bus from Utah."

"Oh dear. It's much too late to do anything tonight. If you'll sit here and fill out these papers you can stretch out and get some sleep. I'll tell security it's OK and they'll keep an eye on you. Then we can start first thing in the morning finding you a place."

I swallowed my disappointment as I said "Thank you" and looked at the immense cavern of rows of long bench seats, mostly empty this time of night. Some were already occupied by sleepers waiting, for various reasons. I was very tired.

A middle-aged lady came over, said "Hi" to the worker. "I just came down to put my boyfriend on the bus back to his base. She turned to me and said "I heard that you're looking for a room and there is an empty room in my building for $12 a week if you could afford that." I nodded that I could. I looked at the worker still holding papers in her hand. She smiled and nodded, "I know Thelma and it's a lucky break for you she was here. It's a safe place."

Thelma smiled "I'm going home now by taxi. You can share the cab if you like, sleep in a bed tonight, and we'll go to the manager tomorrow morning." Already I was loving New York.

My new friend Thelma was true to her word. On the cab ride I gave her my basic situation, and a five minute talk with the Super got her a key. I was taken to a third floor walk-up room where I slept soundly till she knocked on the door next morning. An hour later I had possession of a one room apartment containing a bed, a desk, three chairs, a washstand and a table under the window that folded down when not in use. I had paid for four weeks in advance.

The bathroom, shared by four rooms, was just outside my door, and my window opened on to an open square called an air shaft. As it turned out Thelma's room was directly across the air shaft from me. That's how she knew about the room being vacant. She had lived here three years and told me if I had any problem or questions, I should throw something across into her window.

After I had finished unpacking and had a much needed bath I called across to where she was working in front of her window, and we went out to a coffee shop on the corner. I got directions to the State Employment Services office, to the nearest subway entrance, and details on using this underground transportation system. We walked around the huge apartment complex which was my new home, and I saw the pocket park on the opposite side from our entrance. Down a side street a row of shops included a small grocery and an open-air fruit and vegetable stand. There were several restaurants as well, and Thelma gave me the pluses and minuses of them, including prices.

The rest of day one was spent calling Chuck's contact number from a public phone to give him my address and writing letters home to let our families know I had arrived safely and already found an apartment.

Day two found me at the employment office where I spent an hour with a lovely lady who interviewed and evaluated me. She found three possible positions and set up interviews for the next day. Then she told me to buy a hat and gloves before I went to any of them. The dress I wore was acceptable, but ladies did not go to work without hats and gloves. I walked down 6th Ave from the offices and found a little hat shop where I invested $3.00 of my dwindling funds on a little black cloche hat and black string gloves. I was ready for New York.

The next morning, I dressed carefully in the red suit I had been married in with the black accessories. I pulled my hair back smooth from my face and was satisfied that I looked efficient and mature. I followed directions to the Brooklyn Navy Yard for my first interview and was hired until they heard I was pregnant. They regretted they could not spend time training me when my working time would be limited. The second scheduled appointment went the same way, but the third did not require training and was not physically active so I was hired to start next day. The New York Psychological Testing Corporation graded written tests from schools all over the country. The opening I was to fill was in the Nursing Division and I did well on the speed and accuracy exam. I had a job!

Now I had only to wait until the weekend when Chuck would get leave and come to hear and see what I had accomplished.

CHAPTER 7   Honeymoon

I made sure the room was spotless as could be on Friday afternoon when Chuck was expected. The building was equipped with public phones on each floor, and we had managed to get messages back and forth during the week, and even speak to each other twice. I knew his leave started at four PM on Friday, and the trip from Brooklyn to my location would take the better part of an hour. I was on the sidewalk watching the subway entrance when I saw his tall frame coming up the stairs.

I stood breathless as I saw him for the first time in his sailor uniform. He ran down the block when he saw me and picked me up in a tight hug. We were both talking at once, then started to laugh as he put me down and held hands as I lead him up the steps up to the privacy of our room.

Sometime later we went out and walked around the area, window shopping and soaking in the lights and energy of Manhattan. We ate at the Chock-Full of Nuts restaurant near the apartment where I discovered a nut bread cream cheese sandwich that was ambrosia to me, and he confessed he had learned to love coffee which had never been allowed in his home. The next two days were filled with more of the same. Our time went much too quickly before I had to walk him as far as the subway entrance on Sunday afternoon for his return to base.

This became our routine for the next seven glorious months. I learned to make simple meals after the purchase of a two burner hot plate and a couple of small pots. It was fun finding dishes and utensils for two as I explored shopping areas after work and I made the little apartment bright and cheerful with the addition of pillows and pictures which I found on sale. Chuck brought homework, and I learned some valuable insights into practical medical basics from helping him study. We enjoyed times of reading, talking, and love making between our adventures exploring the city.

Some of the friends he made on base had permanent homes in the metropolitan area and we frequently got invited to informal house parties. The young couples were from many different cultures and backgrounds which led to lively interesting discussions on everything from politics to scientific research. I was especially fascinated by the recent discovery of the miracle drug penicillin. It seems it came from moldy bread and the French use it for healing infections.

I developed new tastes from the variety of foods I was introduced to by the hostesses and the tips I got on motherhood from those who had children were useful. One said "You want to fold the diapers in a triangle. The square kind cause irritation on the legs" while another mother of 2 focused on feeding issues. "Make sure you burp your baby good or they get colic" and "if they don't want to eat put honey on your nipple then they'll take it".

Chuck had a cousin living in the city. They got in touch, and we spent several days with them over our stay. They had one daughter Erica, who was studying abroad to complete her college. She took us out night clubbing when she came in for a visit. Their home was a whole floor of the Sherry Netherland Residential Hotel. Once again, I was introduced to a lifestyle which I always compared to a movie set. Meals were ordered and served, whether cooked in the elaborate kitchen, or brought in from outside. Cousin Charles and Gladys took us to a couple of shows and told stories about life looking out on Central Park.

We took bus rides to strange neighborhoods and walked miles through exotic shopping areas savoring sights, sounds and smells. On those precious weekends we learned to know and love each other as two halves of a tight unit.

During the week I went to work and did my own walking and window shopping. My job was on Fifth Ave surrounded by huge department stores. I learned to look in their cheap basement and reduced areas to find the clothes for my expanding middle. I kept to a strict budget, saving money I would need for my trip home. Chuck gave me what he could from his meager salary, and I managed to put away enough to cover me in Utah for the next four months.

My meals were mostly from sidewalk stands, because I felt uncomfortable sitting alone at a table inside a restaurant. Fruit juice or tea with a piece of fruit or a sandwich or pastry made a healthy and substantial meal. I was a healthy, happy fifteen-year old woman.

Time came to an end the second week of August. Chuck graduated from basic, school, and prepared to be sent to his duty station, destination unknown. I gave notice and said farewells to the people I had worked with the past months, and the super and friends I had made at the apartment building. We scheduled my departure for a Sunday so Chuck could help me to the bus station and wave goodbye. I cried a little before I settled in to watch passing scenery.

Four days later the bus dropped me at a corner near my parents' home with my suitcases. My baby, Donna, was born September fourth.

CHAPTER 8   Motherhood

I spent the required week in the hospital learning the thrilling feeling of feeding my new daughter, exercises to tighten my stomach muscles and the right way to fold and pin diapers. I was told how lucky I was to have no problem with any of it. Donna was 7lbs 4oz of healthy beauty, with a good appetite for my milk, which was plentiful. Since mommy worked at the hospital, she visited every day, and I got very good care and a lot attention.

When it was time to leave the hospital, I discovered my parents had to find a new home. The family they had rented from for past few years were returning to Ogden to enlarge their house and stay there permanently. Mommy worked every day, and Daddy was unpredictable so it fell to me to find something.

With Donna tucked on my shoulder I made the rounds of places I read or heard of, looking for something large enough for four adults and an infant that we could afford. Chuck's parents offered to give me some financial help but Mommy's attitude toward accepting "charity" kept me from accepting their help at this time.

Found it! An elderly couple moving into smaller quarters for their advancing years rented us a large, old, farm style house just at the edge of town center. The property was a full quarter-acre fenced yard and had resisted the encroachment of commercial growth. The couple liked the idea of their home remaining a home. It actually was my parents' home for fifteen years until the couple died within six months of each other.

Mommy was thrilled, "The kitchen is so big! And the pantry too, so everything can be stored out of sight!" Her objection to charity did not extend to used furniture, so she got a large dining room set, including chairs and side buffet from a friend redecorating, and the one we had been using went in the kitchen where we took our normal meals. There was a screened porch across the back of the house, which soon contained an ancient washing machine, a large ice box, and wooden boxes for boots and various tools. Also, neat stacks of wood were stored for the cook stove.

Two bedrooms downstairs went to my parents and my little sister, Lonnie, while the two bedrooms and huge closet upstairs were designated as an apartment for Chuck and me when the war was over. I got a crib for Donna and planned how I would turn this into a welcoming apartment.

Lonnie danced around singing "My own room... I'm gonna put locks on the door so nobody can come in! My own private room." Nobody paid attention but we all shared her joy.

The rest of the house was a large sitting room, where Mommy installed two matching couches and an overstuffed chair, brand new on the payment plan from JCPenney. Across the front a wide porch with roof and pillars furnished a view of passing traffic and the garden which eventually bloomed in the front yard. The back yard had abundant space for planting vegetables and for relaxing.

The bus stop was catty-cornered across the street which made for easy transportation to the hospital for Mommy and railroad station where Daddy had secured a job in the freight yards. This was our perfect home.

I settled in with Donna, and after six weeks got a job as cashier at a grocery store near the house. Either Mommy or Lonnie were usually available to watch her, and they were happy to do so. In case of a problem Chuck's four sisters and his mother were always willing to take over. The whole family settled into a comfortable routine and my nightly letters to Chuck kept him up to date on our progress. He had graduated from pharmacists training and was on a ship in the Atlantic.

Then we got word from him that he was being transferred to the Pacific Theater and would be in Seattle for three weeks before shipping out. Seattle was close! I immediately asked for a week off, bought a train ticket, made arrangements for Donna's care and took off for Oregon.

When I arrived, I got a hotel room near the Navy base and called to let Chuck know where I was. It was a wonderful week, very reminiscent of our New York experience. We ate out and took food back to the room to spend time alone together. We talked endlessly about plans for the future when this separation would be ended. We wandered around the city and the waterfront finding strange shops and cafes. We reaffirmed our love for each other.

Then it was time to go home, for me, and for him to prepare to board his new ship and head toward the Orient.

CHAPTER 9   Peacetime

"It's over! Japan surrendered! We dropped an ATOM BOMB on them and destroyed a big section of the country and we won! It's over, "Lonnie was jumping up and down on the porch yelling the news to me as I pushed my baby in the cradle-swing in the front yard.

I caught my breath as I gently stopped the swing and lifted a now sleeping Donna to my shoulder. I sat on the edge of the porch and thrilled at the implications of this development. Chuck would be coming home! His enlistment was for "duration of hostilities" so he would be discharged after official protocols were completed. I started lists in my mind of what I needed to do to make everything perfect for his return and wiped away tears of happiness at the thought of being together again.

Two months passed quickly as I painted, cleaned, rearranged furniture and made room for his cloths in our limited space. His mother said "Why don't we invite everyone to greet him when he comes in? That way it will all be done at once and he can settle in more quickly." I agreed and we shared the task of contacting all members of both families and planning a homecoming party when we got his scheduled date.

His mother and I took Donna with us when we went to the train station to bring him home. I caught my breath as I saw his tall frame coming off the train. He saw me and running to us with a wide grin held me in a tight hug that lifted me off my feet. He held the baby and played with her on the ride home and stepped out of the car to face both families waiting to welcome him. The sun was shining and lunch was set up in the back yard as everyone shared their news since he has been away.

Our two rooms upstairs were freshly painted with one furnished as a sitting-living room, and the other a bedroom with the baby's crib in one corner. Cooking was done in the downstairs kitchen and carried up or consumed there according to how we felt at the time. I did get a small icebox and carried ice up, for keeping baby food and bottles close. The top of the stairs had been fitted as a closet with a curtain across to cover its contents. It was comfortable and attractive, and Chuck explored all corners repeating "I can't believe you. You did all of this by yourself and taking care of Donna too! It's perfect." I was thrilled at his approval.

I returned to my job; the whole family happy with the baby-sitting arrangements all in place. Chuck slipped easily into the routine. He played with Donna and took over the transportation whenever she needed to be taken anywhere. She thrived, grew active and was happy.

With his pharmacist license from the service, Chuck got a job in the drug store near the house. With the separation check he got, we invested in a good used car, so we no longer had to fit our lives around the bus schedules. We reconnected with old friends and made new ones, and soon began to get involved in socializing. For many events we could take Donna along to play with the children of friends, while at times an ever-ready babysitter was used. The Starlight Ballroom had live bands every weekend in the summer, and we both loved dancing so we went often. The movie theater downtown changed their features every two weeks, so we managed to see a lot of the new movies being made. When winter came, we drove up Ogden Canyon to the Snow Bowl and skied with a group, or sometimes took sleds and kids to nearby hills to initiate them into the job of rolling in the snow.

It soon became apparent that Donna was going to have a little brother or sister, but it didn't interfere with our activities or routines. Others of our friends were also enlarging their families, so I wasn't self-conscious about my expanding girth. We got a new bed for Donna, and the room was large enough to fit it next to the crib, and to accommodate a room divider. Ready.

We went on a long horseback ride into the hills East of Ogden and the next day, I went into the hospital to deliver an 8lb. 4oz. boy. Chuck the second.

CHAPTER 10   Adjustments

I soon discovered that a new baby changes life completely! I stopped working to take care of children, husband and home which cut way back on the time spent going places with friends. Chuck's salary was sufficient to support us, but it needed thoughtful budgeting, a new concept for us. Fourteen month old Donna loved her new brother but needed watching because she wanted to pick him up, put her fingers in his mouth and take his toys and bottle. Our families still were happy to baby-sit when needed but taking care of the two was more challenging than Donna alone.

I developed a pattern of cleaning our apartment after preparing and having breakfast with Chuck, feeding the baby and Donna at the same time. This routine of having meals and sharing time was special for us as a family bonding. After Chuck left for work and our rooms were cleaned, the kids were carried downstairs with laundry, toys and snacks. Weather permitting, we went into the yard after laundry was done and I read books while Donna played and chattered and Chuck napped and gurgled. I weeded and took care of planting and grooming the gardens, planting both flowers and vegetables through the season.

Afternoons brought baths and fresh clothes for me and the kids then getting supper ready before Chuck came home. Generally, the evenings meant playtime for the kids with their daddy, while I cleaned away dishes and laid out clothes and supplies for the morning. Then came our time alone.

When we went out it was usually Chuck's days off and required bags of clothes and bottles and toys, whether we were taking the kids with us or to a sitter. Not a small challenge. "Would you like to come over for a Bar-B-Que and bring your kids?" became the easier and most popular greeting I uttered. Our yard acquired swings, small slides and wading pools to supplement the Bar-B-Que pit and picnic tables already there and became a frequent setting for family and friends.

Chuck's job had him occasionally driving to other locations for products they needed and couldn't wait for mail delivery. Those days he would get home very late but this was the only disruption in our comfortable routine, and we were very happy. The future lay at our feet, and we made plans and dreams of moving into our own home, kids growing up, with all the enthusiasm and indestructible optimism of youth.

Both sets of parents were pleased with us and we maintained close relationships with all of them. All was good in our world…

CHAPTER 11   Daddy's Home

After Donna finished her cereal and tipped the bowl up to get the last of the sugared milk, she climbed onto my lap. Cooing at baby Chuck she stroked his cheek and laughed as he responded by turning his head toward her fingers. I finished my own cereal before settling back to position the baby more comfortably as I held his bottle. He sucked greedily with happy gurgling noises that made Donna laugh as she imitated him. The feeding continued for a half hour with the necessary burping interludes.

I watched the two happy, healthy children and sighed contentedly. I did not regret the decision which had taken me from high school in my sophomore year to marry my first love before he was drafted. I had become pregnant almost immediately and given birth to Donna while he was shipping out to the Pacific. He served his time in the service, and Chuck Junior was conceived during a leave, shortly before his discharge date. I had lived in a small apartment most of the time, returning to my parent's home to turn two upstairs rooms into a separate unit pending Chuck's arrival home. Chuck arrived seven months later.

Now we had settled into a routine of living very different from what either of us was familiar with. Chuck's job as a pharmacist was satisfying for him and provided us with an adequate income for our needs, and we were able to maintain a savings schedule as well. Currently we were looking into finding our own home to rent, with a possible option to buy built into a lease.

"Come on, let's get ready to go out and play. It's a beautiful day." Donna helped carry dishes to the sink and we headed up the stairs to straighten the apartment and dress. I carried Chuck and a basket of sewing, while Donna grabbed a bag with her favorite outdoor toys and we proceeded to the back yard. Donna alternated between digging with a tablespoon in the dirt and chasing a ball around while I stuffed a sock doll with fragrant dried alfalfa, embroidered a face and attached some yarn on top for hair. "Here Chuck, a dolly for you."

His sister giggled as he shook it up and down with a big smile then stuck the top in his mouth and gummed it. "Silly, it's not good to eat!" she said as I gently tugged it out of his mouth and flopped it around.

The day passed and dinner was prepared and ready to be carried upstairs when Donna's "Daddy's home Daddy's home Daddy's home!" sang out as Chuck came in and swept her up in a hug and swung her around a couple of times. Then he came over to kiss me and reach into the baby's seat to tickle his belly. Greetings over we all headed up the stairs with Chuck carrying the roaster in which I had prepared our dinner.

While we were eating, he said "I have to drive up to Idaho tomorrow early. We're out of some stuff we need immediately and the shipment won't get here for another three days. It will be late when I get home so don't wait dinner. I'll get something to eat on the road. Maybe I'll make it before the kids are asleep." This was not an uncommon event since he had advanced and been given more responsibility in his job,

So, I said, "Right, the weather is good so it shouldn't be a bad drive." I kissed him as I started stacking dishes and clearing the room preparatory to bedtime. Chuck played with them and soon was holding both on his lap while he sang nursery rhymes to them. He helped change them into night clothes and carried Donna while I carried Chuck Jr. and settled them in bed.

When we sat and relaxed in the other room he started, "I got out on my lunch hour today and looked at a couple of houses for rent in the area north of the store. One I think is good for us. We can go look at it over the weekend."

"Oohh, how many bedrooms? What's the kitchen like? Is there a big yard?" I bubbled with excited questions as I anticipated the fulfillment of another dream, our own house. Chuck grinned and hugged me as he answered "Two bedrooms and a third slightly smaller room they've been using as an office. I thought we could use it as a bedroom or utility room. A fenced-in back yard with a porch on the back. Most important the rent is affordable. You'll see this Saturday and if you agree we'll work on details and sign a lease." He held me tight in a bear hug till I calmed down, then we went to bed. A happy ending to another day.

CHAPTER 12   Over the Edge

I sat on the edge of the porch watching Chuck Jr. "Chuckie" wiggle in his rocker cradle, and Donna digging in the sand box Chuck had made for her. It was a bright warm morning and I was looking forward to tomorrow when we would see the house Chuck had found for us. From his description last night, it sounded perfect, more than adequate for our little family and for the foreseeable future. I had spoken to Mommy this morning about watching the kids and she was glad to do it. I said, "That's a nice castle you've made Donna. Would you like a story about a queen in the castle? It's almost time to go in for lunch." She turned one last bucket of sand on her castle before she started gathering her toys together to store them on the porch, while I picked Chuckie from his cradle and settled him over my shoulder.

Lunch over, I read the promised story and settled both of them down for naps before sitting down with a magazine. A long afternoon stretched ahead since I knew Chuck would be very late getting home tonight. There were infrequent moments when I felt lonely, since Chuck's job kept him away for longer hours after he was promoted and taking more responsibility. The increased income was welcome, but today I really wanted to tell someone about the probability that we had found a house. I was so full of joy at the idea and full of anticipatory plans I needed a girl friend to share them with. I had friends but getting together had become a major outing not to be taken lightly. It involved packing clothes, snacks, toys and patience so two mothers could spend a few precious minutes catching up on the minutia of our lives. I talked to the kids a lot.

The afternoon passed quietly and with baths and supper over I started getting them ready for the night. I was putting together clothes and supplies for tomorrow's day with Grandma when I heard her come in from work. "Hi Mommy. There's fresh cornbread in the warming oven and my beef stew on the stove. We had supper already but I left it on so you wouldn't have to cook when you got home. When the kids go to sleep, I'll come down and talk for a while."

I tried to judge how long it would take for Chuck to get back from the little town in Idaho where he had delivered some merchandise and picked up some needed supplies. I traced the familiar route in my mind going over the twists and horseshoe curves of Ogden Canyon. I knew that part alone would take an hour and a half, so it would depend on what time he was able to get started for home. I thought, "No matter what time it is he'll be hungry so I'll fix a plate and keep it warm." I got ready to go downstairs.

I checked the baby, sleeping peacefully, and Donna almost asleep, when I heard a knock at the front door and Mommy opening it. Starting down I saw three State Troopers talking with Mommy and my heart squeezed into my throat as they all looked up at me. The words blurred "Swerved on Wiley's curve….another car coming….took two hours to reach….body….."

I heard myself whimpering and felt the fuzzy cotton of my brain rejecting all of it. Then I felt Donna pulling at my skirt and whimpering. The strange voices had made her get up and she was frightened by my anguish. I pulled the little body close and pulled myself together to comfort the child. "It's ok, honey. Just a little accident, but we'll be ok." I thanked the Troopers and said I would be down in the morning to make arrangements.

I heard a loud cry from upstairs as Chuckie woke to no attention and I went up to take care of my baby. Donna followed, proud that she could navigate the stairs without resorting to hands and knees anymore.

I would have time to cry later. Right now, I had a family to attend to.

OWEN

OUR LOVE STORY

Easter 1968

CHAPTER 1 First Date

I stood on my patio and waved as I watched him crossing the parking lot toward my apartment. He was wearing a sport coat and slacks, with a collared shirt and bow tie, in a style at that time was called 'preppie'. I see him with a pipe in his hand, but I'm not sure if that is a true memory or just that I know that at that time he smoked one. I thought he looked so cute; there was a vitality about his bearing that was extremely attractive. And he had the bluest eyes I had ever seen. Not the type of guy I usually went with but he was nice, and it was only for one evening. I greeted him with "Hi, I'm all ready to go. Come in for a minute while I get a sweater. It may be a little cooler on the way home."

We had originally met at Pilgrim State Hospital, where I facilitated a self-help group for patients. I was in the process of introducing the guest speaker for the night when there was a shout from the kitchen area where some of the patients were making coffee for serving after the speaker finished. "Murph, Murph, you son of a bitch. You still owe me for the beer!"

The patient came running toward our speaker bellowing obscenities. As I signaled for security the two were hugging each other and assuring me there would be no bloodshed! By this time the room was in turmoil with the other patients and outside guests milling around trying to determine what the unexpected interruption was about. Security personnel arrived and helped to calm everyone and restore order. We waited for an explanation as the meeting got back on track.

Owen spoke, "Frank and I served in the same paratrooper unit in the Army. We also played in the Army band together and used to take gigs in civilian joints outside the service. And we were drinking buddies."

Frank interrupted with, "This is the guy who turned me on to Turpentine and Codeine when we were broke and out of booze. You just had to go to sick bay and cough."

Owen continued with his talk and the meeting was completed on a positive note. The incident stayed with me as one of those odd coincidences that happen in the treatment facilities. I had never met the young man, Owen, before and since he lived in a different area of the Island it was unlikely, I'd see him again.

I ran into him three months later (July 19, I have no idea why that date has stuck in my mind, but it has) when I was guest speaker at another group. "What are you doing over on the South Shore? I thought you were from Westbury" I asked at the social time after the meeting.

"I was advised to visit some other groups to make some new contacts and get different viewpoints." He answered. we talked a little about our common interests and some common acquaintances. He told me about his friend Frank's continued recovery after discharge from treatment. He also invited me to visit his home group on the North Shore. I did.

When he asked if he could take me to a special event in Mount Vernon, Queens the following Friday I accepted. I had heard a lot about the group but never been there, so I was pleased by the invitation. It was a long drive and it would be pleasant to have someone else drive me. It turned out to be quite a surprise.

When we entered the room, we found four women from his home group already there. They were ladies I had talked with and considered friends, so I didn't understand when they were aloof, almost cold toward us. I was a little hurt that they didn't ask us to sit at their table, but Owen moved on after they ignored our "Hello's" and we found seats nearer to the front of the room.

We both enjoyed the evenings program and the social hour following.

CHAPTER 2   Getting Acquainted

On the trip home from Mt. Vernon we discussed tonight's speakers, the food served at the social hour, and our general feelings about the meeting. I said, "I've never heard anyone who had as many felony arrests and convictions get up and talk about them before!"

He replied, "It's commonly called 'The Cops and Robbers' group exactly because of that. The majority of the members are either police officers or the people they have arrested. These cops spread the hope of recovery by encouraging prisoners to come here after their discharge and guaranteeing them a safe place to be honest about their past. Seems to be very successful."

We shared some details of our own paths in recovery and our general philosophy toward life. I found that though we came from very different backgrounds we shared many of the same ideals and attitudes.

As the drive continued, we talked about our families. I told him about my son, who lived with me and would graduate high school this year. "I'm very proud of Chuck. He has always done great in his grades and also been involved with community groups and sports."

"My daughter, Donna, is two years older and living with my parents in Utah. They flew out there two years ago and she met someone special and decided to stay. Chuck came back alone."

Owen spoke about his two older sisters, and his mother who was living with his sister Joan in Westbury. "The oldest one, Mary, married an army man while he was still in West Point, which was against regulations so they had to keep it secret for almost two years until he graduated. They are living in Texas right now and she's expecting her fifth child. They've moved around a lot over the years and Bill has kept getting promotions. They are very happy."

"Joan stayed home until she was older, when she met her husband Arthur. They bought a starter house in Westbury. They have two teen age girls about the age of your son and have added on to the house. They built a wing for a separate apartment when my mother came to live with them. I have never married; only got involved in recovery from my disease a year and a half ago."

We arrived at my apartment complex and he walked me to my door and said, "I really enjoyed the evening. I'll call you. Good night." He did NOT attempt to kiss me good night. Oh well, I had known it was only for one night.

CHAPTER 3   The Beach

I was really surprised to get a call from him two days later. "I wondered if you'd like to go to Jones Beach Sunday morning. A friend, Ronnie P., has started a meeting there and is asking for support to spread the word. It's early so we could stay for as long as we like."

He picked me up early prepared with a blanket and radio. I had made a picnic lunch and a thermos jug of iced tea, and we went to the meeting at Field ten. About fifteen people were gathered on beach chairs and blankets surrounding an open area of sand, and the speaker was very interesting. I met Ron P. for the first time. "Good luck with this new idea Ron. It's a perfect way to start the day and a new perspective on therapy."

When the meeting ended, we went down the beach to find a spot closer to the water and went in for a swim. We found we both loved swimming and sunshine. We spent a long day talking, and I was fascinated by his broad areas of interest and knowledge. At that time, he was into semantics and the effect of language on the reactions and behaviors of humanity. He was working a minimum wage electronics job in a factory, living in a one room apartment in Westbury, and preparing in a few weeks to start school to finish his college degree which had been interrupted years before by his addiction.

By the time we headed home in the early afternoon we had exchanged information about our respective jobs and schedules. It was certain we would be meeting again. He walked me to my door again and this time he did kiss me goodbye.

CHAPTER 4   Romance

The next day I got a call. "I have to do some wash. Would you like to meet me at the laundromat after work? We could have ice cream while my clothes are washing and then go to a meeting."

"Matter of fact I have laundry too. Sounds like a great idea. I'll see you then." So began our second date and indeed we had sundaes next door while our clothes were washing and drying. Again, we talked and talked and talked. He was still cute, and I found his intelligence and variety of interests endlessly absorbing.

When I folded my laundry, I discovered one of his shirts had wound up in my basket. I ironed it and took it to him when we went to a meeting together the following night. We didn't miss many days seeing each other from that point on.

When I cooked dinner for him, he met my son, Chuck, and they hit it off immediately. Chuck was preparing to leave for college and Owen helped him with some of the forms he had to submit. Chuck had received a scholarship from Brigham Young University in Utah and the paperwork was mountainous. When Chuck left for school Owen drove us to the train in New York City.

We drove up to Greenwich, Connecticut where he had grown up the next day.   He took me to Cos Cob and we visited the house where he was born. "It hasn't changed much." he said. "That big tree by the back window is where I used to climb down to go fishing when I was supposed to be sleeping. The trellises and vines my Grandfather planted around the screen porch have been taken down and they've glassed in the porch."

We didn't attempt to go inside. Instead we went across the street to visit Nick, who was the man that took Owen fishing when he was a boy. Aged and slightly crippled he informed us "I still go out fishing. I can handle the boat if the weather isn't too rough and I still know where the fish hide." We spent an hour while Owen and Nick regaled me with memories of their adventures on Nick's boat years ago.

On our ride home we stopped at a Belmont Racetrack meeting and he got me to my apartment after one am. An exhausting but rewarding day.

CHAPTER 5   Family

The following weekend I met his family. His sister, Joan, lived in Westbury with her husband, Artie, two daughters, Jeanie and Patti, and Owen's mother, Margaret. "We're happy to meet you. Owen has told us about you," was Joan's greeting as she welcomed me.

I got introduced as we went through the house. Artie was cooking in the kitchen as we went through to the back yard where the girls, teenagers, were splashing in the pool. Mary, "Please everyone just calls me Mom," was reading in the shade of a tree.

I felt relaxed and comfortable with his family as we talked and ate through the afternoon. Artie and Joan came out with his delicious culinary offerings. I learned he was graphic artist as his profession and his passions were tennis and cooking. He entertained us by showing how he had trained some of the neighborhoods numerous squirrels to come down and take nuts from his pockets.

When the time came for us to go, I was invited back the following weekend.   As Owen and I drove to our meeting I told him "I like your family a lot. They seem so close and happy together."

"They liked you too. I could tell. You'll be seeing a lot of them from now on."

CHAPTER 6 Married

Owen showed up the next night with a bouquet of four roses and said, "This is in honor of four weeks since our first date."

I know I laughed as I said, "I thought maybe it was your favorite drink!"

"Seriously Lou, why should we pay two rents when we're together every day. Why don't I move in here now that Chuck is gone? We could save money and I wouldn't have to drive home every night."

I felt that tight ache in my throat that brings tears, or laughter, of happiness and answered, "Let's sit down for a minute and talk about it!"

We sat and discussed the details of the move for a long time, I asked, "What about your family. How would they feel about it?"

"They know how I feel about you, and they like you. Only my mother would be upset. She's old and very religious" he admitted, so we decided to tell them we were married in order not to upset his mother.

The following weekend we drove to Cos Cob and stayed for five days exploring the Audubon Center, museums, and visiting people from his childhood who still lived there. September 12 became the wedding date we celebrated for the remainder of our lives together. When we returned home, we announced the "event" by signing his sister's birthday card as Mr. and Mrs. Murphy. He told them the service had been performed by one of the priests who had been his teacher in school. (We had visited this man while we were there). The family was thrilled and wished us every happiness.

He moved from his room in Westbury into my apartment in Farmingdale. He started school to complete the education which had been interrupted by his addiction, and we stalked about all the things we were going to do, the places we were going to go together. God laughed.

By Thanksgiving we knew I was pregnant!!! I remember Thanksgiving dinner at Joan and Artie's with aunts and cousins I hadn't met before all contributing ideas for babies' names. If a girl we settled on Sheryll Louella, (Sheryll was the name of all my dolls when I was little). It was uncle Artie who came up with the boy's name. "I can just see Sean Michael Murphy strutting around in a leather jacket."

In January we got married at the home of a judge in Westbury whom we knew, attended by a friend and his wife and the Judge's two Scottie dogs. We were legally married.

We found and moved into a less expensive but larger apartment in Farmingdale. I learned to budget as I had not done for many years. I stopped work after six months and began collecting furniture for the nursery and sewing and embroidering baby clothes. Life became focused around the impending event, Owen's school and work schedule, our recovery meetings and time spent with friends. Friends included his family who were thrilled and wonderful.

Sean Michael Murphy arrived the 24th of June.

CHAPTER 7   Challenge and Joy

Birth control pills were new and no one mentioned sometimes woman's bodies overcome them; they didn't work for everyone. I was faithful to my routine and still found myself pregnant six months later. We prepared to welcome another baby.

Owen got advancement at his job, while continuing evening classes at Hofstra University, then rushing home to spend precious time with Sean and me. We managed to get to our recovery groups three or four times a week, taking Sean with us or dropping him off at Joan and Artie's where they were all delighted to baby-sit.

I worked hard at learning to keep house and care for the active baby boy I had. "Agnes has a smaller crib to give us that will fit along this wall, so I moved Sean's crib to the other side. The big mobile I'll hang up in this corner where they both can see it." "Peggy gave me 4 yards of flannel to make baby clothes, and some velour that I'll use to a make jacket for Sean." Our conversations also included the child rearing philosophies he was learning in some of his classes.

We knew we had a challenge when Sean stood up at six months and walked at seven! He never crawled, just ran. He adored his father and when Owen was home, they were inseparable. That was a wonderful summer. Chuck came home with his brand new bride Linda and worked with Owen for the summer. Linda also got a temp job for the summer, and we all spent time at the beach, parks, and with family and friends. Sean was the center of everything and they loved him. When it was time for them to drive back to school in Utah, I spent their last day helping them pack and doing last minute shopping. Their last goodbye was, "Linda is pregnant. We're so impressed with Sean we want one like him."

I had suffered with a backache and cramps through the day. "I did too much running around carrying Sean all day." That night it got worse and we barely made it to the hospital in time for me to deliver not one, but two girls four minutes apart. So Sheryll got my favorite name for my dolls when I was a kid, Sheryll, and Faye, my mother's name, and Louella became Louella Margaret, after Owen's mother.

CHAPTER 8   Family Grows Up

The apartment was now too small for the increased number so with Joan and Artie's help we got a house in Suffolk County, in Central Islip which was still almost a farming community. It was a "fixer upper" with two bedrooms and an upstairs which could, and became, finished and utilized as two more bedrooms. The yard was overgrown with wild roses which took more than two years to be dug out and replaced with vegetable gardens. We moved in the middle of December.

We had all kinds of ideas about the improvements we were going to make. Thirty-seven years later when we sold it, I remembered all those ideas, most of which had been downsized or abandoned. It was a happy house.

In March I developed a prolapse which required major surgery including a hysterectomy. The Doctor said, "You must spend six weeks away from the children in order to ensure healing. You can't lift anything heavier than a cup of coffee!"

The twins, seven months old, went to a friend who had four teenagers to spoil them. Sean, now twenty-one months, went to a different friend with six children from five to fourteen. A bright spot was the birth of Linda's boy on the day of my surgery. My first grandson, Jeff, was born seven months after his aunts.

Owen learned to study with one baby on each shoulder and a book in his hands. And he never dropped one. We sometimes took turns sleeping, went through infant surgeries on both girls, measles for Sean, falls, scrapes, blood, fevers, fights, chicken pox for all of them, music lessons, wrestling, twirling, boy scouts, girl scouts, etc, etc, etc... we all survived.

One of our major treats through the years started when the girls were two years old. Owen's friend said "You guys are going to have breakdowns if you don't get a vacation. I'm paying for a week at the YMCA family camp, and I'll loan you five sleeping bags. Our family loved it but they're grown now."

We went to YMCA family camp every fall for a week through the kids growing up years and starting the following year a ski trip every Christmas and Easter break. When they became teens, the trips included their friends.

Owen shouted "I graduated! Got my degree and I already accepted a job I was offered." He became a teacher first of English then Math. He continued taking courses until he had collected two Master's Degrees, which increased pay scale as high as it could go.

I got involved with PTA when the kids entered school took and courses in first aid until I had achieved an EMT certification, so I was ready to hear from a friend in my recovery program, "I can get you into our counseling program but you need a high school diploma."

I got my GED and went back to school, to find I really liked the counseling and psychology courses. I got a job that I kept for twenty-five years, retiring on my seventieth (70) birthday. We managed throughout to maintain close contact with our recovery support system and needed them when living pressures became intense.

After the kids entered high school Owen came home one day with a book of discount coupons and we decided on a place we would like to try. As we sat in a new Mexican Restaurant he observed, "Do you realize this is the first time since Sean was born that we have ever gone to a restaurant without them!" We decided to go out once a week until we had used up all the coupons.

It felt strange at first but we both loved to travel and took advantage of the many opportunities that began to present themselves. I got involved with the National Counselors organization and was sent to conferences in San Diego, San Francisco, Milwaukee, Orlando, Niagara Falls, and many places in upstate New York. Owen loved exploring the new towns while I was working, then showing me what he had found when I was free.

Elderhostel did a presentation at his school and he came home all excited. "It's for people over sixty so you're old enough and I can go as your guest. Look at all the different things they offer and they're cheap. We could go to two a year!" We made sixteen trips with Elderhostel, all with a music theme, in many different locations. The first was to Nova Scotia, then Montreal, Quebec, North Carolina, Florida, Arizona and more than I can even remember. We skied the Laurentians and the Berkshires, swam, canoed rapids on the Delaware and Colorado rivers, rode horseback through forests and visited museums and ruins.

We lived a full, active, interesting middle age.

CHAPTER 9   Process of Aging

Owen had developed diabetes in his late forties, but after we found the cause of his mood swings, unstable temper and lethargy it offered no major disruption. We carefully monitored his insulin schedule and I began to study nutrition and exercise in order to understand and help him control it. His doctor at the time said, "If you're having a hot fudge sundae take extra." He took his insulin shots regularly (mostly) and followed his diet (mostly). It interfered with our lifestyle not at all and seldom affected our personal relationship.

On a conference trip to Lake Placid, Owen was thrilled at the run around Mirror Lake. He liked it so much we rented a rowboat after I had finished my work for the day and rowed all the way around it. After that came a banquet followed by a walk around the town before heading for bed. He woke me at 3 AM with "My stomach and my arm are killing me, owww it hurts!"

I called an ambulance and we went to the emergency room where it was diagnosed as heart attack. The E.R. doctors said, "It's common for people to forget the elevation and thinness of the air and to overdo exercise."

I don't know when the memory lapses started, and I don't know how long they had been happening before I found out. I was having a hot chocolate break at the ski lodge on Catamount Mountain in Massachusetts when I saw him coming off the expert slope. When I went out to meet him, he said, "I know you. Where are we?" He was in a complete fog but recognized that I was with him. He didn't know his name or have any reference points.

I just kept talking and he gradually began to come back. I got him into the car but when I said, "we'll be at the hospital in ten minutes, just relax." He objected.

"It's happened before and it goes away. I'll be ok in a little while."

I took him to a local recovery meeting where we listened and relaxed a little. Afterwards I asked, "What would like to eat? Chinese, Mexican or Friendly's?" We got Chinese and had dinner and watched TV in the motel. It was more than two hours later before he seemed normal again, remembering who he was and where and why we were here and what he could recall of what had happened. He told me then that he had experienced previous episodes of "blacking out" for short periods.

We returned home and got to our G.P. who diagnosed it as Transient Ischemic Attacks otherwise known, I discovered, as small strokes. She didn't seem too worried by it and put him on blood pressure meds.

At the end of that year he announced he was going to retire a year earlier than he had planned because of changes in administration and teaching methods. I believed him because I had been experiencing some of the same issues at Malloy College where I had been teaching part time for fifteen years. Now I'm sure it was more because of memory lapses and balance problems.

He disclosed, "Dr. Khominini diagnosed me with Parkinson's Disease over a year ago but I've not had any problems. But she's now concerned about a heart valve that might need attention." He had just bought a new rototiller so he could enlarge his garden. All good reasons to retire.

Six months after he retired, he had an aortic valve replacement and one week later developed a cardiac tamponade. His chest had to be reopened to drain the fluid around his heart. That was twenty-three days in hospital and put major stresses on the entire family. He joked, "Dr. Blake promised to put in a zipper for easier access." I took some time off when he came home, but his recovery was rapid. It was only three months before he was fully active again with permission to resume all physical activity.

We flew in August to an Elderhostel program at Oak Creek Canyon, Arizona. It is between Sedona and Flagstaff and the itinerary offered lectures on Indian history and traditions, and visits to local habitats includind the Grand Canyon and Sedona. In our down time we visited my eldest daughter, Donna and her husband Carl, who lived just below Sedona. At the close of the Elderhostel we stayed on with them an extra four days and explored Montezuma Wells where they lived. Owen enjoyed every part of it and continued to increase his activity levels.

Over the next two years he started running again and bought a treadmill so he could run in the garage in bad weather. A couple of times he got "lost" on his neighborhood runs. He began to tell me about these incidents, and they were becoming too frequent. One day he moaned, "help me Lou! I can't stand up!" I helped him to the car and stayed in the room when the Doctor spoke to him. For the first time I heard what she had been telling him and found out what he had NOT been telling her.

From that time on I went into all medical appointments with him and kept track of signs and symptoms as we went for neurological, psychological and finally psychiatric evaluations. I submitted my resignation to be effective on my seventieth birthday. It quickly became apparent it was not safe to leave him alone for very long, and my birthday coming in six weeks seemed the appropriate time.

There were no pots left without holes in the bottom because Owen would forget he had something on the stove. One night I came from work and detected an overwhelming stench in the house. In the kitchen I discovered a blacked pot on a burner in which six eggs had boiled dry and exploded all over walls and ceiling. Owen was in his computer room and greeted me with, "I thought I'd start making a salad for dinner so I boiled some eggs." He was completely unaware of anything amiss.

I didn't let him see me crying as I made a bean salad for dinner. "I think I'll paint the kitchen over the weekend. It could use it!", and I did.

My retirement party was fun and filled the Irish Coffee Pub where it was held. I got nice gifts and nice speeches from Brother Joe, with whom I gone to school twenty-five years before, Marion Goldman, head of Molloy College continuing education, Barbara Maurer, supervisor of Suffolk Probation's Alcohol Treatment Program, and several of my co-workers. It was a memorable ending to a chapter of my life. The food was good too.

And now I was free!

CHAPTER 10   Another Life

For another year I continued to teach some courses at Molloy College, and to keep up with some of the activities of the Counselors Association. Our daughter Sheryll with her two toddlers would stay with Owen, and he loved playing with his grandchildren. All three of our kids were married but Louella lived in Florida and Sean in Canada.

We took trips every two months for a couple of years. When Owen was making retirement plans, he said "I've made a budget for six week-long trips every year for five years!" We were able to take all the family to Kauai, including Sean and his wife Chelley, Sheryll with Laura (6) and Dylan (3), and Louella. Neither of the girl's husbands could take time from their work to come on the trip. We stored memories that will never fade.

We climbed to the Fern Grotto where Elvis Presley filmed his famous Hawaiian wedding picture, then returned to our condo and watched the movie. We heard, "The beach is closed. There's a seal sleeping there and the area is roped off so no one can disturb it!" We immediately walked down to the beach to join others watching from a safe distance the huge animal snoozing comfortably on the sand. We traveled to the other side of the island to picnic at the lagoon that inspired Peter, Paul and Mary, looking across the clouds that hung low over it, to write "Puff the Magic Dragon." We fed a stray cat that adopted us for the week and he became comfortable enough to come sit by Dylan, who would sit very still in order not to scare him away.

We spent a week with Chuck and his wife Linda in California boating on a small lake and exploring a horse breeding ranch. We managed an overnight trip Las Vegas where I gorged on fabulous ninety0nine cent buffets while Owen and Linda spent their allotted funds on the gaming tables.

Visits to daughter Donna and husband Carl in Arizona included scenic tours and getting better acquainted with my two granddaughters and great grandchildren. Marla has one son, and Tara has three sons and one daughter. They both had homes near their mother and spent much time together. Owen was able to enjoy all these activities, sometimes with a wheelchair and a lot of help from willing volunteers.

During this time, we continued to take advantage of Elderhostel trips and make plans for the time when we would be old. We saw a lawyer and prepared Living wills, power of attorney designations, details on the limits of treatment we desired, including DNR certificates. We also visited a local mortuary and paid for the funeral services we chose. We wanted to spare our children some of the grief we had both experienced with the deaths of our own parents.

A period of beautiful memories and new perspectives.

CHAPTER 11   Decline

Owen fell on the treadmill one morning and hurt his back. He was in constant pain and the clinic we belonged to gave him muscle relaxants and pain pills, which did nothing. Finally, I took him to my chiropractor, whom I was convinced was a miracle worker. Turned out I was right. She had her own x-ray machine in her office and would not do intensive work without pictures. After she looked at Owen's pictures she said, "I can't touch him! You get to a spine specialist STAT! He has fractured cervical vertebrae." She called a center for us and got an immediate appointment.

Two weeks later he had spinal surgery, and never had pain in his back again, although he never returned to the level of physical activity he had formerly enjoyed. This had more to do with his cognitive decline than any muscular problem. At physical therapy he complained, "They want me to go up and down these steps thirty times! It makes me too tired, and then they try to get me to ride a bicycle!" He refused and wouldn't stand up until I agreed to take him home.

On our last trip to Hawaii he went to the men's room on the way home and turned the wrong direction coming out. I missed seeing him and he was on his way out the gate when the loudspeaker broadcast, "Owen Murphy please report to nearest Airport Personnel. Owen Murphy your plane has been called, please report to Airport personnel." I had become concerned and asked for help. They got him there and we barely made the plane.

Another fun travel story was when he went for a stroll in Florida and forgot where and who he was. He sat down on the grass at the side of the street, and when people asked if he needed help said, "No thanks, just resting." It was a resort area, not a neighborhood where people sat on the grass so soon a police officer came and asked for identification. The officer recognized the resort from the keycard, which was the only thing he had with him, and drove him home. He never went walking alone again.

We managed a family vacation in Orlando with all three children and Sheryll's three, Laura and Dylan with her stepson Brian, and his friend Molly. Sean and Chelley were able to come from Canada and Louella drove over from her home in Clearwater. It was a wonderful week for all with some memorable moments. We had suites at two different resorts with Owen and I sharing one with Sean and Chelley, and the rest of the group sharing a larger one. Sheryll cooked a spaghetti dinner one evening and we were all sitting around the table when someone noticed Owen was trying to wrap his pajama string around his fork. "I dropped some spaghetti and I was just trying to get it up." We helped him.

One night Chelley woke to some noise in the kitchen at three AM and got up to see Owen preparing to pour water into the toaster. He wanted to make coffee and thought it was the coffee maker. After that we unplugged everything before we retired. He had reached a point of needing a wheelchair for transport but could navigate inside by pulling himself around holding onto furniture. He was able to go swimming and enjoyed the warm Florida pools. He loved Sea World, especially the manta ray pool where he could sit and let the soft animals swim around his hands.

In those couple of years, we made trips to visit my son and daughter-in-law chuck and Linda in California, my daughter and son-in-law Donna and Carl in Arizona, and to our son Sean (and Chelley) in Canada and our daughter Louella in Florida. There were side trips to Los Angeles, the Grand Canyon, Niagara Falls and Tampa Zoo associated with those trips.

There were some tense moments during Owen's periods of memory loss and stubborn hallucinations but generally he loved seeing all the stimulating sights and experiences we had.

CHAPTER 12   Living with Alzheimer's

Five years from my retirement date we sold our home, after thirty-seven years.   It became apparent I could no longer safely care for him and the house, since my arthritis had reached the point where my second hip needed replacement. Our daughter Sheryll was in the process of a divorce, so we built an apartment in the den of her house. By my design there was no stove, only a small refrigerator and separate freezer. We had microwave, toaster oven, electric fry pan and coffee pot, etc. All things I could unplug at bedtime.

We were able to help Sheryll keep her home, and we got a safe place to care for ourselves. All things worked as they were meant to.

Owen loved watching cartoons with his grandchildren. He sat on the floor to play Barbie and Ken stories with Laura when she came home from kindergarten in the afternoon. During the day Dylan stayed with us and had long conversations with grandpa. They shared peanut butter-banana sandwiches and cheese and cracker plates. They talked about our trips to Hawaii and planned for when we would go again.

2:30 AM. I woke suddenly and saw Owen's bed was empty! In our small three rooms there was little danger, but he had fallen several times recently and it was becoming increasingly difficult to get him up. So I rushed to the kitchen and ….. stopped. Over the countertop and floor were the dozen eggs that had been in the refrigerator, and Owen was standing at the sink washing the toaster. "I got hungry so I was just making some breakfast."

4 AM, another night. I looked around the limited corners of our apartment and couldn't find him, so I opened the door to the basement, went halfway down the steps and called, "Owen are you down here?" No answer. Next, I went to the door to Sheryll's house and upstairs. The door opening woke her and she joined the search.

We looked outside, then finally she went all the way down into the basement. She found him in the room-sized cedar closet lying on the floor on a pile of clothes. When she tried to get him up, he said "I'm just resting here a while. I'll get up later."

1:30 AM I heard a crash and jumped up to find 'what now'. The noise came from upstairs in Sheryll's kitchen and she was coming down from her bedroom. Owen was sitting on the floor with her oven door in his lap. "I had a little trouble putting the bread in." he said. We helped him downstairs and back to bed, and next morning called someone to replace the oven door.

3:00 AM Owen was gently shaking me. "I can't start the car, something's wrong with it." I fought my way up from the fog of sleep to see him in pajamas and robe holding my car keys in his hand. ARHHHH! It was 15 degrees outside but he kept insisting, "The class will get out of hand if I don't get back. My lunch hour is over, don't you understand? I have to get back to my students." I looked outside to see the car door standing open, so obviously he had been trying unsuccessfully to start it. Thank Goodness! He had given up driving more then seven years before and had never driven this Saturn which was only three years old. It took longer than usual to convince him that school had been cancelled due to the weather and get him back to bed.

5:00AM I normally don't get up till 5:30 but I saw that Owen was up so I grabbed a robe as I jumped out of bed, just in time to see him going out the door. Grabbed a coat and ran after him asking, "Where are you going?"

"I thought I'd go for a walk." I did not respond with my usual communication skills.

"Are you nuts? It's the middle of the night! You'll get frostbite!", meanwhile he continued walking down the street with me behind him waiting for him to fall. As I was able to regain some sanity, I began to quietly ask him "Do you think maybe this is far enough?" We passed four houses before he concluded that it was enough. He walked back and sat at the table waiting for breakfast to be ready.

Our next-door neighbor said he saw Owen come out alone and was going to come out until he saw me following him. He figured I could handle it. We called a locksmith that day and had locks put on the three doors in our apartment. I kept them locked and wore the keys on a ribbon around my neck from then on. The second set of keys went to Sheryll.

Falls were mostly in the confines of our apartment because when we went out to doctors, family affairs, recovery meetings and the spiritual fellowship we had joined, the Gathering of Light, he was always in a wheelchair. He enjoyed everything, especially the Gathering of Light singing. He would doze off during the talking but come alive when the music started. He could remember the words to songs when he couldn't remember my name.

He became convinced his address was in Connecticut, where he was born, and sometimes refused to get out of the car when we arrived home. "Not our house!" After frustrating hours of argument, I started just letting him sit in the car for a time, then when I asked if he was ready to come in for lunch, etc. it would usually work. If Sheryll was home she could get him to do whatever. For me it was, "Stop ordering me around!" "You think you know everything!" "You always have to control everything!" Guilty as charged, I'm afraid.

CHAPTER 13   Assisted Living

A crash woke me. I saw Owen on the floor struggling to pull himself up on the bed. "I just wanted to get up and I tripped. I'm sorry I woke you up." There was a lot of blood and I saw he had fallen on the corner of his nightstand and had a large gash just above his left eye.

I ran for cold wash cloths and applied pressure. "Just relax Owen, it's ok. I need to stop this bleeding, so just lean back against the bed and relax. Okay, is that better?"

Sheryll came down and saw the bleeding was still heavy so she called the ambulance. The hospital closed the wound with seventeen stitches and kept him for two days of testing to make sure there were no additional injuries.

It had become obvious I could no longer keep him safe at home, but since he could still feed himself and get to the bathroom (sometimes) insurance criteria said he didn't qualify for a nursing home. Sheryll said, "We have to find out what's available for Alzheimer patients!" We investigated and found an assisted living home in the next town with a separate section for Alzheimer and other dementia patients.

The cost was daunting but I figured out, "The IRA that was meant to last till we were ninety will pay for his care for two years. That will give us time to figure out what comes next."

Owen loved it there. His room was large and cheerful and the staff attentive and pleasant. Food was tasty and plentiful and therapists came to the ward three times a week with songs, games and art projects. Everyone participated at their own level and in the beginning, Owen was active with all the activities. I visited every other day and got to know the staff and other patients. Owen said, "we have to tell everyone about this resort. It's so nice and the service is so good." Yes, it was.

He was there a year and two months during which he was hospitalized three times with different traumas. He got flu twice in spite of receiving flu shots. We had to wear masks and gowns when we visited and I remember our grandson Dylan took this very seriously. He kissed Grandpa through the mask and washed his hands a lot so he wouldn't give Grandpa any germs.

He fell and broke a hip and they repaired it with pins, which relieved his pain. Much less traumatic than a hip replacement.

At the second upper respiratory infection it was discovered he had a MRSA staph infection. After this period of quarantine, the assisted living facility couldn't take him back so the hospital got him into a nursing home in Cold Spring Harbor. This was July seven.

CHAPTER 14   The Final Chapter

We were very fortunate to get what I think is one of the best nursing homes. The staff loved him, and treated him, and all their patients, with respect and dignity regardless of their condition. I was welcome to visit at any time and got to know staff, other patients and their families. I liked being there at lunch time and helping to serve. I also helped feed Owen, which he frequently needed. "Ok now Owen, you've been chewing that mouthful for a long time. Try to swallow now. See." And I would massage downward on his throat till he swallowed, then give him another mouthful to chew.

He still recognized me although when asked he would say, "oh that's my mother. She takes care of me." or, "My little sister, a pain in the neck sometimes!" He always gave his address as the Greenwich, Connecticut house where he was born and grew up. The staff thought it remarkable that I made the drive every day until I corrected their impression.

One incident – I came into the day-room and leaned down to kiss his forehead. Another patient at his table yelled, "Kiss me! Kiss me too."

Owen tried to stand. "NO! She's Mine! She belongs to ME." So be it.

We were on our way to Thanksgiving dinner with his family when Sheryll's cell phone rang. "This is Ann O-Conner at the nursing home. Owen was just transported to the hospital. He went into a coma at lunch time."

Sheryll turned the car around took me home to my car, and I went to the hospital while she took the kids out to the family. She brought the kids up to see Grandpa late that evening. At one point he opened his eyes a little while Laura was talking to him and seemed to be trying to smile. I like to remember that his last look was at Laura and Dylan, the grandchildren he so loved. His eyes never opened again.

The next day the Doctor and Social Workers talked to me about the papers on file, the health care proxy and living will we had made six years previously. They required the removal of the feeding tubes inserted when he was admitted, which were keeping his body alive. There was nothing more to be done at the hospital so he was returned to the nursing home. On Friday and Saturday, I spent most of the day talking to him and reading to him at his bedside. On Saturday his niece Patty came up and spent some time with us.

In the late afternoon I went home expecting to return in the morning. At nine-fifteen the phone rang and nurse O'Conner said, "Come now. It's time." Sheryll drove, and we walked into his room to find the nurse sitting by his bed holding his hand. He had just passed. She said, "I've been holding his hand for the last hour. I had a feeling and there was nothing else I could do."

It's a visual I will always remember; the nurse sitting by the bed holding his hand. She had been fond of telling him Irish jokes since his original admission, sometimes getting a response.

That was November 27, 2007. We had been married forty-three years.

EPILOGUE

LIFE GOES ON. I have stayed close and had the support of family and old friends and new, in our recovery program and the community groups I've found along the way. I am blessed to be able to be active in all of these although age is beginning to limit physical participation.

It took two years for me to learn to cook for one, budget and handle now very limited finances and debts, and get used to the hole left by the loss of one who had been half of me for so many years.

I still visit Calverton Cemetery on a regular basis to talk to you for a little. I take your favorite flowers in season and leave a stone to remind you I was there. My thing.

A couple of years ago I a beautiful sunny February day to explore the North Shore after I left Calverton. I passed the famous bakery where on weekends cars and limos line up to get the "best pies on the East Coast."

I stopped at Bed and Breakfast place in Greenport where we got a gift of a weekend and spent an October weekend lying on the beach and exploring a small nearby lighthouse.

Stopped again at the little homemade ice cream store where we had seen an Academy Award winning actress in sweats and no make up pull up in her limo and come in to get cones for her two kids and her driver. The ice cream was really good.

I drove to the pier where we had sat outdoors and chased saucy gulls away from our fish dinners and checked that our special little tearoom was still open. I spent some time revisiting the Indian Museum and stopped at the park where we had picnicked in past years.

One day of reliving and re-feeling memories. There are so many wonderful memories I'm left with. We did so much and lived so fully I need to express my gratitude to the spirit that gave us our lives together.

Made in the USA
Middletown, DE
06 January 2020